THE LITTLE BOOK
OF COLOURING

ON SAFARI

PEACE IN
YOUR POCKET

Other books in
THE LITTLE BOOK OF COLOURING
series:
Animal Kingdom
In Bloom
Tropical Paradise
Patterns
Into the Deep
Wild Woodland

Published in the UK in 2016 by
Quercus Editions Ltd
Carmelite House
50 Victoria Embankment
London EC4Y 0DZ

An Hachette UK company

A CIP catalogue record for this book is available
from the British Library

ISBN 978 1 78648 076 7

10 9 8 7 6 5 4 3 2 1

Designed and typeset by Carrdesignstudio.com

Printed and bound in the UK by Clays Ltd, St Ives plc

THE LITTLE BOOK
OF COLOURING

ON SAFARI

PEACE IN
YOUR POCKET

ILLUSTRATED BY
AMBER ANDERSON

Quercus

I took a walk in the woods and
came out taller than the trees.

Henry Thoreau

In order to see the birds it is necessary

to become a part of the silence.

Robert Lynd

There are always flowers for those

who want to see them.

Henri Matisse

The journey of a thousand miles

begins with a single step.

Lao Tzu

We are chameleons, and our partialities

and prejudices change place with

an easy and blessed facility.

Mark Twain

No man ever steps in the same river twice,

for it's not the same river and

he's not the same man.

Heraclitus

If you truly love nature,

you will find beauty everywhere.

Vincent van Gogh

If you don't have a memory like an elephant,

leave an impression like one.

Anonymous

I felt my lungs inflate with the onrush

of scenery – air, mountains, trees, people.

I thought, 'this is what it is to be happy'.

Sylvia Plath

In order to carry a positive action

we must develop here a positive vision.

Dalai Lama

The trees, the flowers, the plants grow in silence. The stars, the sun, the moon move in silence. Silence gives us a new perspective.

Mother Teresa

To the eyes of the man of imagination,

nature is imagination itself.

William Blake

I adore simple pleasures. They are

the last refuge of the complex.

Oscar Wilde

The man who has confidence in himself

gains the confidence of others.

Hasidic proverb

The wasted of all days

is one without laughter.

E. E. Cummings

You cannot always wait for the perfect time,

sometimes you must dare to jump.

Anonymous

Like all great travellers, I have seen
more than I remember, and remember
more than I have seen.

Benjamin Disraeli

A lion sleeps in the heart of every brave man.

Turkish proverb

To move, to breathe, to fly, to float,

To gain all while you give,

To roam the roads of lands remote.

To travel is to live.

Hans Christian Andersen

The earth has music for those who listen.

Shakespeare

Monkey see, monkey do.

Proverb

We travel not to escape life but for life not to escape us.

Anonymous

In all things of nature there is

something of the marvellous.

Aristotle

Come forth into the light of things.

Let nature be your teacher.

William Wordsworth

No bird soars too high if he soars

with his own wings.

William Blake

I go to nature to be soothed and healed,

and to have my senses put in order.

John Burroughs

When you do something noble and beautiful
and nobody noticed, do not be sad. For the
sun every morning is a beautiful spectacle
and yet most of the audience still sleeps.

John Lennon

The creation of a thousand forests

is in one acorn.

Ralph Waldo Emerson

The poetry of the earth is never dead.

John Keats

We can't choose where we come from

but we can forge our own path forward.

Anonymous

I travel for travel's sake.

Robert Louis Stevenson

Adventure is not outside man; it is within.

George Eliot

The truth is like a lion. You don't have to defend it. Let it loose. It will defend itself.

Augustine of Hippo

I loved the stars too fondly

to be fearful of the night.

Galileo

It is better to conquer yourself

than to win a thousand battles.

Buddha

Nature does not hurry, yet

everything is accomplished.

Lao Tzu

Nothing behind me, everything ahead of me,

as is ever so on the road.

Jack Kerouac

Living at risk is jumping off the cliff and

building your wings on the way down.

Ray Bradbury

We cannot see our reflection in running water.

It is only in still water that we can see.

Taoist proverb

The things that make me different

are the things that make me.

A. A. Milne

Jealousy is a tiger that tears not only its prey
but also its own raging heart.

Anonymous

Nature does nothing uselessly.

Aristotle

Nature never did betray

the heart that loved her.

William Wordsworth

Look deep into nature, and then you will
understand everything better.

Albert Einstein

Happiness demands more on the inward

deposition of mind than on outward

circumstances.

Benjamin Franklin

Hope is the thing with feathers

That perches in the soul.

Emily Dickenson

Come and join
THE LITTLE BOOK
OF COLOURING
community online!

Ⓟ pinterest.com/mindfulcolour

❖

Share your favourite illustrations,
find out more about the benefits of
colouring and mindfulness and get
inspired for your next creative project.

Quercus